BEYOND THE HIGH HILLS

Beyond

PHOTOGRAPHS BY Guy Mary-Rousselière

the high hills

A BOOK OF ESKIMO POEMS

THE WORLD PUBLISHING COMPANY · CLEVELAND AND NEW YORK

COWP

PUBLISHED BY The World Publishing Company

2231 WEST 110TH STREET, CLEVELAND 2, OHIO

PUBLISHED SIMULTANEOUSLY IN CANADA BY

Nelson, Foster & Scott Ltd.

Library of Congress Catalog Card Number: 61-14072

2 3 4 5 65 64 63 62

KNUD RASMUSSEN, *Johan Victor* *1879-1933,* the Danish explorer who first collected and translated the poems in this book, has noted that the Eskimo language does not include a word for "inspiration" in the sense that we understand it. Instead, the Eskimo uses a simple phrase meaning "to feel emotion," and since every human being will feel many emotions in the course of his lifetime, "all human beings are poets in the Eskimo sense of the word."

So there are no individual authors for the poems in this book. They are really songs, chanted spontaneously to celebrate the hunt or other adventures, great sorrow or great happiness, or merely the joy of being alive. As such they are remarkable for their clarity of thought and preciseness of image. As Rasmussen points out in referring to the poem on page 13, it is "nothing more than a scrap of nursery rhyme, known to children at play, yet it shows to the full the high level of Eskimo poetry."

These poems were collected among the Iglulik Eskimos of the Hudson Bay region and the Musk Ox people of the Copper Country and appear in volumes 7 and 9 of Rasmussen's *Report of the Fifth Thule Expedition, 1921–1924.* The photographs by Father Guy Mary-Rousselière, who is an Oblate priest doing mission work among the Eskimos, were taken in the same area.

I arise from rest with movements swift

As the beat of the raven's wings

I arise

To meet the day.

My face is turned from the dark of night

To gaze at the dawn of day,

Now whitening in the sky.

I will walk with leg muscles

which are strong

as the sinews of the shins of the little caribou calf.

I will walk with leg muscles

which are strong

as the sinews of the shins of the little hare.

I will take care not to go towards the dark.

I will go towards the day.

There is joy in

Feeling the warmth

Come to the great world

And seeing the sun

Follow its old footprints

In the summer night.

There is fear in
Feeling the cold
Come to the great world
And seeing the moon
—Now new moon, now full moon—
Follow its old footprints
In the winter night.

Hard times, dearth times

Plague us every one,

Stomachs are shrunken,

Dishes are empty. . . .

Mark you there yonder?

There come the men

Dragging beautiful seals

To our homes.

Now is abundance

With us once more,

Days of feasting

To hold us together.

Know you the smell

Of pots on the boil?

And lumps of blubber

Slapped down by the side bench?

Joyfully

Greet we those

Who brought us plenty!

13

I sighted a bear

On the drifting ice,

It seemed like a harmless dog

That came running towards me gladly,

So eager was it to eat me up on the spot,

That it swung round angrily

when I swiftly sprang aside out of its way.

And now we played catch-as-catch can

From morning to late in the day.

But by then it was so wearied

It could do no more,

And I thrust my lance into its side.

Here I stand,

Humble, with outstretched arms.

For the spirit of the air

Lets glorious food sink down to me.

Here I stand

Surrounded with great joy.

And this time it was an old dog seal

Starting to blow through his blowing hole.

I, little man,

Stood upright above it,

And with excitement became

Quite long of body,

Until I drove my harpoon in the beast

And tethered it to

My harpoon line!

I could not sleep,
For the sea lay so smooth
near at hand.
So I rowed out,
and a walrus came up
close beside my kayak.
It was too near to throw,
And I thrust the harpoon into its side,
and the hunting float bounded over the water.
But it kept coming up again
And set its flippers angrily
like elbows on the surface of the water,

trying to tear the hunting float to pieces.
In vain it spent its utmost strength,
for the skin of an unborn lemming
was sewn inside as a guardian amulet,
and when it drew back, blowing viciously,
to gather strength again,
I rowed up and stabbed it
With my lance.
And this I sing
because the men who dwell
south and north of us here
fill their breathing with self-praise.

The great sea

Has sent me adrift

It moves me as the weed in a great river,

Earth and the great weather

Move me,

Have carried me away

And move my inward parts with joy.

Bring hither your wooden ornament,
I will deck myself with it,
To make me look like a real woman.

Glorious it is to see

The caribou flocking down from the forests

And beginning

Their wandering to the north.

Timidly they watch

For the pitfalls of man.

Glorious it is to see

The great herds from the forests

Spreading out over plains of white.

Glorious to see.

Glorious it is to see

Early summer's short-haired caribou

Beginning to wander.

Glorious to see them trot

To and fro

Across the promontories,

Seeking a crossing place.

Glorious it is

To see the long-haired winter caribou

Returning to the forests.

Fearfully they watch

For the little people,

While the herd follows the ebb-mark of the sea

With a storm of clattering hooves.

Glorious it is

When wandering time is come.

The lands around my dwelling

Are more beautiful

From the day

When it is given me to see

Faces I have never seen before.

All is more beautiful,

All is more beautiful,

And life is Thankfulness.

These guests of mine

Make my house grand.

All unexpected I came and took by surprise
The heedless dweller of the plains,
All unexpected I came and took by surprise
The heedless dweller of the plains,
And I scattered the herd
In headlong flight.

I came creeping up along over the marsh
With bows and arrows in my mouth.
The marsh was broad and the water icy cold,
And there was no cover to be seen.
Slowly I wriggled along,
Soaking wet, but crawling unseen
Up within range.
The caribou were feeding, carelessly nibbling the
*   juicy moss,*
Until my arrow stood quivering, deep
In the chest of the bull.
Then terror seized the heedless dwellers of the
*   plain.*
The herd scattered apace,
And trotting their fastest, were lost to sight
Behind sheltering hills.

When I was young,
every day was as a beginning
of some new thing,
and every evening ended
with the glow of the next day's dawn.

26

Do not weep, little one,
Your mother will fetch you,
Mother is coming for you
As soon as she has finished
Her new kamiks.

Do not weep, little one,
Your father will fetch you,
Father is coming as soon as he has made
His new harpoon head,
Do not weep, little one,
    Do not weep!

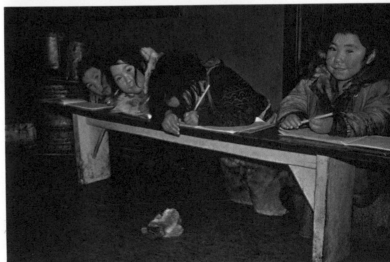

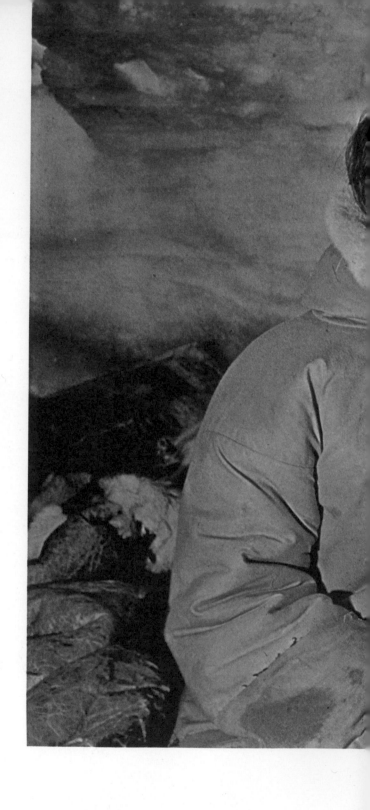

When I chance to think of my childhood
and recall all the old memories from those days,
then youth seems a time
when all meat was juicy and tender,
and no game too swift for the hunter.
Now, I have only the old stories
and songs to fall back upon.

Far, far will I go,
Far away beyond the high hills,
Where the birds live,
Far away over yonder, far away over yonder.

Two pieces of rock barred the way,
Two mighty rocks,
That opened and closed
Like a pair of jaws.
There was no way past,
One must go in between them

To reach the land beyond and away,
Beyond the high hills,
The birds' land.

Two land bears barred the way,
Two land bears fighting
And barring the way.
There was no road,
And yet I would gladly pass on and away
To the farther side of the high hills,
To the birds' land.

DEAD MAN'S SONG

DREAMED BY ONE WHO IS ALIVE

I am filled with joy
When the day peacefully dawns
Up over the heavens.
I am filled with joy
When the sun slowly rises
Up over the heavens.

But else I choke with fear
At greedy maggot throngs;
They eat their way in
At the bottom of my collarbone
And in my eyes.

Here I lie, recollecting
How stifled with fear I was
When they buried me
In a snow hut out on the lake.

A block of snow was pushed to,
Incomprehensible it was
How my soul should make its way
And fly to the game land up there.

The door-block worried me,
And even greater grew my fear
When the fresh-water ice split in the cold
And the frost-crack thunderously grew
Up over the heavens.

Glorious was life
In winter,
But did winter bring me joy?
No! Ever was I so anxious
For sole-skins and skins for kamiks.
Would there be enough for us all?
Yes, I was ever anxious.

Glorious was life
In summer,
But did summer bring me joy?
No! Ever was I so anxious
For skins and rugs for the platform
Yes, I was ever anxious.

Glorious was life

When standing at one's fishing hole

On the ice.

But did standing at the fishing hole bring me joy?

No! Ever was I so anxious

For my tiny little fishhook

If it should not get a bite.

Glorious was life

When dancing in the dance-house,

But did dancing in the dance-house bring me joy?

No! Ever was I so anxious,

That I could not recall

The song I was to sing.

Yes, I was ever anxious.

Glorious was life . . .

Now I am filled with joy

For every time a dawn

Makes white the sky of night,

For every time the sun goes up

Over the heavens.